Standardized Test
Skill Builders
for Reading
Grades 3–4

S C H O L A S T I C
PROFESSIONAL BOOKS

New York • Toronto • London • Auckland • Sydney
Mexico City • New Delhi • Hong Kong

Cover design by Jaime Lucero & Kelli Thompson
Interior design by Creative Pages, Inc.
Interior illustrations by Kate Flanagan

ISBN 0-439-16230-0

Contents

Introduction to Teachers

We all know how important it is for students to do well on tests. This book is one in a series designed to help you help your students become better test takers. Your students will learn strategies that will help them apply essential reading skills to a standardized test format.

In the past few years, many statewide tests and national standardized tests have undergone significant changes, not just in *what* they measure but also in *how* they measure content and skills. The examples and practice tests in this book reflect the latest developments in testing and are designed to look like the state and national tests. Features include:

- A variety of different types of literature and informational texts
- A combination of multiple-choice and short-answer questions
- Integrated questions measuring both reading and language arts

This book covers all of the significant reading and language arts skills tested on the five most widely used standardized tests: the *CTBS TerraNova, Metropolitan Achievement Test, Stanford Achievement Test, Iowa Test of Basic Skills,* and *California Achievement Test.* It also uses the same kinds of questions and the same formats as the standardized tests.

Practice Activities

There are six Practice sections in this book, followed by a full-length Reading Test. Each Practice focuses on specific reading strategies and skills and includes related questions on vocabulary, composition, grammar and usage, capitalization, punctuation, or spelling. Features of each Practice include:

- Sample items for students to work through
- Hints on how to answer each type of question
- Explanations of the correct answers
- Reminders to help students during an actual test
- A Practice Test to help students apply what they have learned

Procedures

We recommend that you first teach the targeted reading skills before you use this book. Then work through each Practice Sample with your students. Using the overhead with transparencies of assigned pages helps students understand the process of thoroughly reading passages and accurately answering the questions. Discuss the sample questions and how to get the right answers, and then have students take the Practice Test. Use the Answer Key at the back of the book to score each test, or have students score the tests themselves and record their scores in the box at the end of each Practice Test. Either way, make sure students have ample opportunity to study their own tests and learn from any mistakes they might have made. When students have completed all the practice activities, administer the Reading Test (beginning on page 35). The Reading Test has five selections and a total of 36 items. It will take about one hour to complete.

Students who complete the activities in this book will become familiar with the kinds of questions they will see on "real" tests, and they will have a new arsenal of techniques and strategies for achieving better test scores.

PRACTICE 1: SAMPLE

Directions
Read the passage. Choose the best answer to each question.

HINT: Read the title and the whole passage to decide what the passage is mostly about.

Running From Danger

Does a frightened ostrich really hide its head in the sand? No, this idea is <u>erroneous</u>. No one has ever seen an ostrich with its head in the sand. But a frightened ostrich is likely to crouch and stretch its neck out along the ground. From this position, the ostrich can watch whatever frightened it. If the danger comes closer, the ostrich runs away. Since an ostrich can run as fast as 50 miles an hour, its chances of escaping are very good.

A   **What is this passage mostly about?**
Ⓐ how a frightened ostrich behaves
Ⓑ how fast ostriches can run
Ⓒ why an ostrich digs in the sand
Ⓓ what enemies an ostrich has

HINT: Look back at the passage to find the answer to each question.

B   **When danger comes close, an ostrich**
Ⓕ hides its head.
Ⓖ fights back.
Ⓗ runs away.
Ⓙ kicks sand.

C   **The passage says, "No, this idea is <u>erroneous</u>." What does <u>erroneous</u> mean?**
Ⓐ dangerous
Ⓑ wrong
Ⓒ interesting
Ⓓ clever

D   **Find the sentence that is complete and is written correctly.**
Ⓕ An ostrich watches from a distance.
Ⓖ On the ground, in a crouch.
Ⓗ A lion or maybe even a person.
Ⓙ Approaching the nervous ostrich.

Finding the Answers to Practice 1: Sample

The most important idea in a passage is the *main idea*. It may be clearly stated in the passage, or you may have to figure out the main idea from the information given. Questions about the main idea may ask you to choose a main idea sentence, the best title, or a main topic that tells what the passage is mostly about. Other questions may ask about supporting details that tell about the main idea.

To answer question **A**, you must decide what the passage is mostly about. You are looking for the main topic. This passage explains that a frightened ostrich doesn't really hide its head in the sand. Then it tells how an ostrich really does behave when it is frightened. The correct answer is **A**.

To answer question **B**, you must find the supporting detail that tells what an ostrich does when danger comes close. Since the passage states that the ostrich runs away, the correct answer is **H**.

For question **C**, you must figure out what erroneous means from the way it is used in the passage. The first sentence asks if a frightened ostrich puts its head in the sand, and the next sentence gives the answer: "No, this idea is erroneous." This suggests that erroneous means "wrong," answer **B**.

Question **D** is a question about writing complete sentences. A complete sentence has a subject, which tells what the sentence is about, and a

predicate, which tells what the subject is or does. Answer **F** is correct because it is the only choice that has both a subject (*an ostrich*) and a predicate (*watches*).

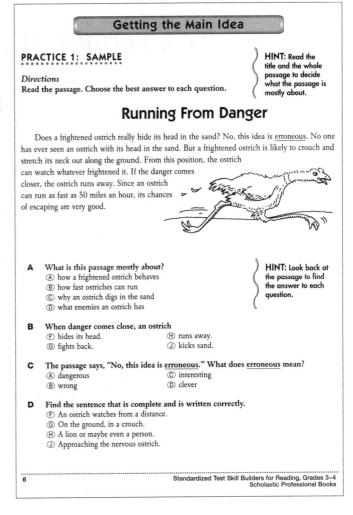

Getting the Main Idea

PRACTICE 1: SAMPLE

HINT: Read the title and the whole passage to decide what the passage is mostly about.

Directions
Read the passage. Choose the best answer to each question.

Running From Danger

Does a frightened ostrich really hide its head in the sand? No, this idea is <u>erroneous</u>. No one has ever seen an ostrich with its head in the sand. But a frightened ostrich is likely to crouch and stretch its neck out along the ground. From this position, the ostrich can watch whatever frightened it. If the danger comes closer, the ostrich runs away. Since an ostrich can run as fast as 50 miles an hour, its chances of escaping are very good.

A What is this passage mostly about?
Ⓐ how a frightened ostrich behaves
Ⓑ how fast ostriches can run
Ⓒ why an ostrich digs in the sand
Ⓓ what enemies an ostrich has

HINT: Look back at the passage to find the answer to each question.

B When danger comes close, an ostrich
Ⓕ hides its head.   Ⓗ runs away.
Ⓖ fights back.   Ⓙ kicks sand.

C The passage says, "No, this idea is <u>erroneous</u>." What does <u>erroneous</u> mean?
Ⓐ dangerous   Ⓒ interesting
Ⓑ wrong   Ⓓ clever

D Find the sentence that is complete and is written correctly.
Ⓕ An ostrich watches from a distance.
Ⓖ On the ground, in a crouch.
Ⓗ A lion or maybe even a person.
Ⓙ Approaching the nervous ostrich.

6   Standardized Test Skill Builders for Reading, Grades 3–4
                                               Scholastic Professional Books

REMINDERS: As you take the Practice Test, remember these hints.

✔ Read the title and the whole passage carefully.

✔ Look at the picture. Sometimes a picture gives clues to what the passage is about.

✔ Decide what the whole passage is mostly about.

✔ Look back at the passage to find the answer to each question.

✔ Look for clues in the passage to figure out the meaning of a word you don't know.

PRACTICE 1: TEST

Directions
Read each passage. Choose the best answer to each question.

The Farmer and the Volcano

There are volcanoes all over the world. Some have been still for thousands of years. Others erupt from time to time. Every once in a while, a new volcano is born. This happened in 1943 in a village in Mexico. A few days before the volcano erupted, a farmer named Dionisio Pulido was working in his field. He noticed that the ground was getting warmer. Several days later the field cracked open! Steam and melted rock sprayed into the air. Then the ground began to bulge. The flat field grew into a hill. It grew higher and higher as the eruption of ash and lava continued. Dionisio Pulido's farm and village were covered with ash and rock. This eruption finally stopped in 1952, and the volcano has been still ever since.

1   What is the main idea of this passage?
  Ⓐ Most volcanoes have been still for thousands of years.
  Ⓑ A new volcano erupted in a village in Mexico in 1943.
  Ⓒ Dionisio Pulido lost his farm in Mexico.
  Ⓓ A volcano erupts with ash and lava.

2   What is another good title for this passage?
  Ⓕ "The Birth of a Volcano"   Ⓗ "Volcanoes Around the World"
  Ⓖ "Farming in Mexico"   Ⓙ "Up on a Hill"

3   What did Dionisio Pulido notice when he was working in his field?
  Ⓐ His field had a crack in it.
  Ⓑ A volcano had stopped erupting.
  Ⓒ His field was covered with ash.
  Ⓓ The ground was getting warmer.

4   The passage says, "Then the ground began to bulge." What does bulge mean in this sentence?
  Ⓕ sink   Ⓗ disappear
  Ⓖ swell up   Ⓙ cool off

Kids Against Trash

Keeping our environment clean is a big job, but there are ways for kids to help. For example, do you bring a bag lunch with a juice box to school every day? In one school year, that adds up to a lot of bags and empty juice boxes in the trash. But you can do something about this. Just switch to the kind of bag and drink cup that you can reuse every day. Get your friends to switch, too. Together you can really make a significant difference. You and your friends can also form a trash patrol in your neighborhood. Get together once a week to pick up paper, cans, and bottles. You may even be able to recycle this trash for money. Then you and your friends can share the profits.

5 **What is the main idea of this passage?**
- (A) Kids can help keep the environment clean.
- (B) People throw out paper, cans, and bottles.
- (C) Lots of kids have joined trash patrols.
- (D) Neighborhoods are easy to clean up.

6 **What is this passage mostly about?**
- (F) making money
- (G) eating lunch at school
- (H) taking care of trash
- (J) getting together with friends

7 **This passage tells kids to use lunch bags and drink cups that**
- (A) are made from paper.
- (B) don't cost too much money.
- (C) can be reused.
- (D) don't need to be washed.

8 **The passage says, "Together you can really make a significant difference." What does significant mean in this sentence?**
- (F) amusing
- (G) important
- (H) ordinary
- (J) famous

9 **Which sentence should come first in the paragraph?**

_____. They come in every shape and color you can imagine. Some of these animals swim, and others creep along the ocean floor. Some animals never move at all.

Ⓐ Oceans cover most of the earth.
Ⓑ Many different animals live in the ocean.
Ⓒ Fish can live in rivers, lakes, or oceans.
Ⓓ The ocean is a mysterious place.

10 **Choose the pair of sentences that best support this topic sentence.**

A starfish is a fascinating sea creature.

Ⓕ I caught a starfish once. Most starfish have five arms.
Ⓖ A starfish has eyes and feet on its arms. If an arm falls off, it grows back.
Ⓗ Starfish eat shellfish. These include oysters, clams, and scallops.
Ⓙ Most starfish live about four years. Some may live to be seven years old.

11 **Find the sentence that is complete and is written correctly.**
Ⓐ The biggest animal in the world.
Ⓑ Not a giant dinosaur.
Ⓒ A blue whale is nearly 100 feet long.
Ⓓ Living in every ocean.

12 **Find the sentence that is complete and is written correctly.**
Ⓕ A sea cucumber is not a vegetable.
Ⓖ An animal with a long, round body.
Ⓗ Rows of tube feet and a mouth at one end.
Ⓙ Crawling in sand or mud.

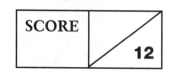

SCORE

12

PRACTICE 2: SAMPLE

HINT: Scan the passage first to see what it is mostly about. Then read it carefully.

Directions
Read the passage. Choose the best answer to each question.

The Family Musician

When Ina was ten, she joined the school band. Her friend Val had already joined, and Ina didn't want to miss the fun. But band was not fun for Ina. She did not have much talent as a clarinet player, and she hated practicing. Even to her, the music she made sounded awful. Ina tried to quit, but her dad would not let her because he loved having a musician in the family.

Then one day something terrific happened. Ina's brother Kyle sneaked into her room and started playing her clarinet. Unlike Ina, Kyle really enjoyed himself and even taught himself to play a few tunes. At dinner that night, Kyle told Ina and Dad what he had done. Ina was delighted. She told Kyle to keep the clarinet. Then she smiled at Dad and said, "It's great having a musician in the family, isn't it!"

A **What did Ina do first in this story?**
  Ⓐ She gave her clarinet to Kyle.
  Ⓑ She joined the school band.
  Ⓒ She practiced her clarinet.
  Ⓓ She decided that being in the band was not fun.

HINT: To find the information you need, look for signal words, such as *first, then, because, like,* and *unlike.*

B **Why did Dad stop Ina from quitting the band?**
  Ⓕ He wanted a musician in the family.
  Ⓖ He thought she enjoyed the band.
  Ⓗ He knew she was very talented.
  Ⓙ He wanted her to make new friends.

C **How was Kyle different from Ina?**
  Ⓐ He was not interested in music.
  Ⓑ He knew she was very talented.
  Ⓒ He thought the band was awful.
  Ⓓ He liked playing the clarinet.

D **The story says that Ina joined the band. What does band mean in this story?**
  Ⓕ a thin, flat strip of material
  Ⓖ to mark with stripes
  Ⓗ to join together in a group
  Ⓙ a group of musicians

Finding the Answers to Practice 2: Sample

To understand text, you must figure out how ideas are related to one another. Ideas in a passage are often related by sequence of events, by cause and effect, or by comparison and contrast.

Question **A** is a question about the sequence, or time order, of events in the passage. The question asks what Ina did first, and it lists four things she did. Since joining the school band was the first thing Ina did in the story, the correct answer is **B**.

Question **B** is about cause and effect. To answer the question, you must understand why Dad stopped Ina from quitting the band. The passage says he would not let her quit *because* he loved having a musician in the family. Dad's wanting a musician in the family is the cause, and stopping Ina from quitting is the effect. Answer **F** is correct.

Question **C** asks how Ina was different from Kyle. According to the passage, Ina hated practicing the clarinet. But, *unlike Ina*, Kyle really enjoyed playing it. The correct answer is **D**.

Question **D** is about using context clues to figure out the meaning of a word that has more than one definition. The word *band* has several meanings, as in "*rubber band*," "a *band* of thieves," "to *band* together." In this story, *band* means "a group of musicians," answer **J**.

PRACTICE 2: SAMPLE

HINT: Scan the passage first to see what it is mostly about. Then read it carefully.

Directions
Read the passage. Choose the best answer to each question.

The Family Musician

When Ina was ten, she joined the school band. Her friend Val had already joined, and Ina didn't want to miss the fun. But band was not fun for Ina. She did not have much talent as a clarinet player, and she hated practicing. Even to her, the music she made sounded awful. Ina tried to quit, but her dad would not let her because he loved having a musician in the family.

Then one day something terrific happened. Ina's brother Kyle sneaked into her room and started playing her clarinet. Unlike Ina, Kyle really enjoyed himself and even taught himself to play a few tunes. At dinner that night, Kyle told Ina and Dad what he had done. Ina was delighted. She told Kyle to keep the clarinet. Then she smiled at Dad and said, "It's great having a musician in the family, isn't it!"

A   **What did Ina do first in this story?**
  Ⓐ She gave her clarinet to Kyle.
  Ⓑ She joined the school band.
  Ⓒ She practiced her clarinet.
  Ⓓ She decided that being in the band was not fun.

HINT: To find the information you need, look for signal words, such as *first, then, because, like,* and *unlike.*

B   **Why did Dad stop Ina from quitting the band?**
  Ⓕ He wanted a musician in the family.   Ⓗ He knew she was very talented.
  Ⓖ He thought she enjoyed the band.   Ⓙ He wanted her to make new friends.

C   **How was Kyle different from Ina?**
  Ⓐ He was not interested in music.   Ⓒ He thought the band was awful.
  Ⓑ He knew she was very talented.   Ⓓ He liked playing the clarinet.

D   **The story says that Ina joined the band. What does <u>band</u> mean in this story?**
  Ⓕ a thin, flat strip of material   Ⓗ to join together in a group
  Ⓖ to mark with stripes   Ⓙ a group of musicians

REMINDERS: As you take the Practice Test, remember these hints.

✔ Scan the passage first to see what it is about and how it is organized.

✔ To find the information you need, look for signal words that indicate:
- sequence of events (*first, then, later, before, after, finally, last*).
- causes and effects (*because, so, since, as a result*).
- comparison/contrast (*like, unlike, same as, different from, however, but, both*).

✔ For words with more than one meaning, try each meaning in the sentence and choose the one that sounds correct.

PRACTICE 2: TEST

Directions
Read the passage. Choose the best answer to each question.

The Boy Who Asked Questions

Thomas Edison may be the greatest inventor who ever lived. The electric light bulb made Edison famous, but he came up with more than a thousand other inventions. He also figured out ways to make other people's inventions work better.

Thomas Edison's success probably didn't surprise his parents. From the time he could talk, he asked questions about the world around him. When his parents didn't know an answer, Thomas did experiments to find the answer himself. Mr. and Mrs. Edison allowed the experiments as long as they were safe. They knew how bright their son was and how much he loved learning.

When he was seven, Thomas started school. Although he was bright, he had an awful time. His teacher was strict. He believed children should listen, not ask questions. The children had to sit still and straight at their desks. No experiments were allowed! After only three weeks, Thomas refused to go to school anymore. His mother, who had been a teacher herself, agreed to teach him at home. Mrs. Edison believed in making her son's lessons fun. She found books she knew would interest him, and she let him do science experiments in the basement.

Thomas's home lessons ended when he was 12. For a few years he worked on a train. The electrical telegraph machines he saw in train stations fascinated Thomas, so he became a telegraph operator. In his free time, he tried out his own electrical inventions.

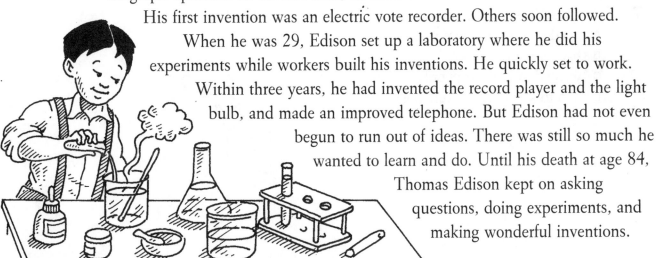

His first invention was an electric vote recorder. Others soon followed. When he was 29, Edison set up a laboratory where he did his experiments while workers built his inventions. He quickly set to work. Within three years, he had invented the record player and the light bulb, and made an improved telephone. But Edison had not even begun to run out of ideas. There was still so much he wanted to learn and do. Until his death at age 84, Thomas Edison kept on asking questions, doing experiments, and making wonderful inventions.

1 Both as a young child and as an adult, Thomas Edison

- Ⓐ was famous.
- Ⓑ loved learning.
- Ⓒ was lazy.
- Ⓓ worked on a train.

2 The passage says, "He also figured out ways to make other people's inventions <u>work</u> better." In which sentence does <u>work</u> have the same meaning?

- Ⓕ We will <u>work</u> until two o'clock.
- Ⓖ Being a teacher is hard <u>work</u>.
- Ⓗ <u>Work</u> the clay with your hands.
- Ⓙ Show me how these tools <u>work</u>.

3 When his parents could not answer one of his questions, Thomas would

- Ⓐ look for the answer in a book.
- Ⓑ ask his teacher the same question.
- Ⓒ do an experiment to answer the question.
- Ⓓ ask them a different question.

4 The passage says, "Although he was <u>bright</u>, he had an awful time." What does <u>bright</u> mean in this sentence?

- Ⓕ smart
- Ⓖ shiny
- Ⓗ very clear
- Ⓙ cheerful

5 When Thomas was 12, he

- Ⓐ became a telegraph operator.
- Ⓑ set up his own laboratory.
- Ⓒ went to work on a train.
- Ⓓ made an improved telephone.

6 Thomas Edison's first invention was the

- Ⓕ electric light bulb.
- Ⓖ record player.
- Ⓗ telegraph machine.
- Ⓙ electric vote recorder.

7 Thomas Edison kept inventing for the rest of his life because he

- Ⓐ needed to make more money.
- Ⓑ had so many ideas.
- Ⓒ wanted to impress people.
- Ⓓ had to keep his workers busy.

8   How was Thomas's education at home different from his experience at school? Write one or two sentences telling how they were different.

_____

_____

_____

_____

Directions
Read each pair of sentences. Choose the sentence that best combines the two sentences into one.

9   Young Thomas loved science.
     He loved reading, too.
   Ⓐ Young Thomas loved science and he loved reading.
   Ⓑ Young Thomas loved science and reading.
   Ⓒ Young Thomas loved science, he loved reading.
   Ⓓ Young Thomas loved reading science.

10   Edison invented the light bulb.
      Edison did not discover electricity.
   Ⓕ Edison invented the light bulb, but he did not discover electricity.
   Ⓖ Edison invented the light bulb, he did not discover electricity.
   Ⓗ Edison invented the light bulb or did not discover electricity.
   Ⓙ Edison invented the light bulb and discovered electricity.

Directions
Find the word or words that best complete(s) each sentence.

11   Edison thought the record player was his _____ invention.
   Ⓐ fine   Ⓒ finer
   Ⓑ most finest   Ⓓ finest

12   Workers could build Edison's inventions _____ than he could.
   Ⓕ quickly   Ⓗ more quickly
   Ⓖ quickest   Ⓙ most quickly

SCORE
        12

Making Inferences

PRACTICE 3: SAMPLE

Directions
Read the passage. Choose the best answer to each question.

HINT: Before you read, take a quick look at the questions so you know what to look for in the story.

The Turtle on the Bank

"Look at that big old turtle!" Leah cried out as she pointed to the creature on the shore. She and Matt paddled toward the riverbank. As they got closer to the shore, Matt reached out and gently poked the turtle with his paddle.

"Yikes!" he exclaimed as the turtle snapped at the paddle. "Did you see that? It crushed the wood. Look at the hole in my paddle!"

"It must be a snapping turtle," Leah said. "As Grampa would say, that's the turtle's way of telling us it was here first. I think we should leave it alone."

"I agree," said Matt. "Let's get out of here."

A **What will most likely happen next?**
  Ⓐ The turtle will bite Leah.
  Ⓑ Matt and Leah will paddle away from the turtle.
  Ⓒ Matt will try to catch the turtle.
  Ⓓ Leah will poke the turtle with her paddle.

HINT: Look for clues in the story to help figure out the answers.

B **You can tell from this story that Matt and Leah are in a**
  Ⓕ sailboat.   Ⓗ train.
  Ⓖ car.   Ⓙ canoe.

C **Who is Matt?**
  Ⓐ the turtle   Ⓒ Leah's father
  Ⓑ Leah's grandfather   Ⓓ Leah's brother

D **Find the word that best completes the sentence.**

The turtle crawled into the water and _____ into the mud.
  Ⓕ disappear   Ⓗ disappeared
  Ⓖ disappearing   Ⓙ will disappear

Finding the Answers to Practice 3: Sample

To make inferences, you must "read between the lines." For example, if a character in a story looks outside in the morning and sees puddles on the street, you can *infer* that it rained the night before. Inferences are not stated in the story; you must figure them out from what you know.

To answer question **A**, you must predict what will happen next. At the end of the story, Leah and Matt agree that they should leave the turtle alone. Matt says, "Let's get out of here." Based on these clues, the most likely answer is **B**, "Matt and Leah will paddle away from the turtle."

To answer question **B**, you must look for clues. The story suggests that Matt and Leah are on the water, and it says that they paddle toward the riverbank, so they are probably in a canoe. Answer **J** is correct.

For question **C**, you must look for clues to help you draw a conclusion about Matt. The story does not tell you who Matt is, but you know he is not the turtle (choice A) or Leah's grandfather (choice B). Leah refers to Grampa as if Matt knows him, so Matt is probably Leah's brother, answer **D**.

Question **D** is a question about using verbs correctly. The verb you choose should be in the same tense as *crawled*. "The turtle *crawled* into the water and *disappeared* into the mud." The best answer is **H**, "disappeared."

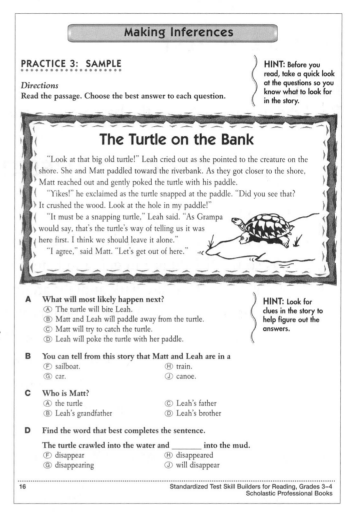

REMINDERS: As you take the Practice Test, remember these hints.

✔ Take a quick look at the questions first. Then read the whole passage carefully.

✔ Look for clues in the passage to help answer the questions.

✔ Go back to the passage to find the information you need.

✔ When you draw a conclusion, look for two or more details in the passage to support your answer.

PRACTICE 3: TEST

Directions
Read the passage. Choose the best answer to each question.

Salamander Crossing

Dear Maxine,

I knew that living at Aunt Grace's house for a few weeks would be weird. I was so right! I think I'm going to hate it here. Her house is way out in the middle of nowhere. It's really dark at night around here with no streetlights and hardly any cars on the road. At first I thought it would be quiet, but it's not. It's especially noisy at night! That's because of the spring peepers.

"What is a spring peeper?" you might ask. It's a tiny frog that sings a very loud song at this time of year. There must be hundreds of them. I hope I can sleep with all that "peeping" going on.

Danny

Dear Maxine,

Today everyone is all excited about salamanders. I've never even seen a salamander. Aunt Grace showed me pictures. Salamanders are little animals with short legs and long tails. They look sort of like Pete's pet lizard, but they are smooth and black with blue spots.

The telephone keeps ringing. "Tonight's the night," everyone is saying. It's cold out, and it's raining like crazy. Aunt Grace invited another family over for supper, so she's making a big pot of soup. She made me try on all the old raincoats and boots around here so that I could pick out something to wear tonight. We're all supposed to go outside after supper. I can't believe they expect me to go out on a dark, cold, rainy night to look for slimy little salamanders. Now I know I'm going to hate it here. As I said, this place is really weird!

Danny

Standardized Test Skill Builders for Reading, Grades 3–4
Scholastic Professional Books

Dear Maxine,

Last night was totally amazing! After supper, everyone put on rain gear. We took flashlights and went out to the road. Other people were there already, and there were little lights shining everywhere. Families were coming to watch for salamanders.

Salamanders usually stay under leaves and logs. People hardly ever see them. But in the woods behind Aunt Grace's house, there is a little pond that fills with water in the spring. Every year, salamanders go there to find mates and lay eggs. The odd thing is, they all go there on the very same night. It is always on the first rainy night at the end of winter, after the ice has melted. That's how everyone knew that last night would be the night.

Soon we started seeing salamanders—first one, then two more. Our job was to watch them cross the road and to place a small red marker beside the road each time one crossed. Some people had the job of blocking the road. No cars are allowed to go there on the night of the salamander crossing.

The road was shiny and wet, and so were the salamanders. It was fun to see those little guys crawl out of the woods one after another! I put eleven markers by the road. The markers are for a town salamander count. People will know from counting the markers how many salamanders live around here.

After about three hours, we went inside to get warm. We drank cocoa and ate popcorn and joked and laughed. I'll never forget the night of the salamander crossing. Maybe if I'm lucky, I can help count salamanders again next year.

Danny

1   **You can tell that Aunt Grace lives**
   ⒜ in a city.
   ⒝ on a farm.
   ⒞ in the desert.
   ⒟ near the woods.

2   **The salamanders crossed the road to**
   ⒡ find a new home.
   ⒢ get to the pond.
   ⒣ look for a dry place.
   ⒥ find food.

3   **In what month does this story probably take place?**
   ⒜ January
   ⒝ March
   ⒞ June
   ⒟ September

4   **Imagine how the road near Aunt Grace's house looked the next morning. What would someone see?**
   ⒡ a line of salamanders
   ⒢ people with flashlights
   ⒣ puddles and red markers
   ⒥ piles of ice and snow

5 Which statement about the people in the town is most likely accurate?

   Ⓐ No one in the town really cares about the salamanders.

   Ⓑ Everybody feels that peepers and salamanders are annoying.

   Ⓒ Most of the people like rainy nights better than clear nights.

   Ⓓ Everybody enjoys the night of the salamander crossing.

6 Each letter is addressed to Maxine. Maxine is probably

   Ⓕ Danny's mother.   Ⓗ Danny's teacher.

   Ⓖ a friend back home.   Ⓙ a pet.

7 Write one or two sentences comparing how Danny felt at the beginning of the story with how he felt at the end.

_____

_____

_____

_____

Directions

Choose the word or words that best complete each sentence.

8 Aunt Grace _____ a big pot of soup.

   Ⓕ make   Ⓗ making

   Ⓖ makes   Ⓙ have made

9 Danny and Maxine _____ good friends.

   Ⓐ is   Ⓒ being

   Ⓑ was   Ⓓ are

10 Danny counted the markers after the salamanders _____ the road.

   Ⓕ cross   Ⓗ had crossed

   Ⓖ were crossing   Ⓙ will cross

SCORE	
	10

PRACTICE 4: SAMPLE

Directions
Read the passage. Choose the best answer to each question.

HINT: Look for clues about how the characters feel and where the story takes place.

The Older Girls

Annika climbed on the school bus and sat behind Dee and Pam. Annika liked being around these two sixth graders. They acted cool and said such clever things. Annika couldn't wait to be three years older so she could be just like Dee and Pam.

As the bus rolled down the road, Annika pretended to doze off. But she was all ears as Dee and Pam talked.

"I can't sleep over Friday night," Dee was telling Pam. "I have to baby-sit for my little brothers."

"That's okay," replied Pam. "I'm way behind on my science report. I have to work on it all weekend."

The older girls kept talking, but Annika wasn't listening anymore. Baby-sitting for little brothers! Working all weekend on a report! Maybe being older would not be so terrific after all.

A **How does Annika feel about Dee and Pam?**
- Ⓐ She dislikes them.
- Ⓑ She thinks they are lazy.
- Ⓒ She thinks they act silly.
- Ⓓ She admires them.

B **Where does this story take place?**
- Ⓕ in a school
- Ⓖ on a bus
- Ⓗ at Dee's house
- Ⓙ at the library

HINT: To understand the plot of a story, think about the main character's problem or conflict and how it is solved.

C **At the end of the story, Annika decided that**
- Ⓐ Dee and Pam were not as nice as she had thought.
- Ⓑ she needed to find some jobs as a baby-sitter.
- Ⓒ being a sixth grader might not be as much fun as she thought.
- Ⓓ Dee and Pam were waiting for her to say hello.

D **Annika "was all ears" means that she**
- Ⓕ had large ears.
- Ⓖ listened closely.
- Ⓗ heard someone talking about her.
- Ⓙ put her hands over her ears.

E **Find the word that best completes the sentence.**
Annika saw the older girls and sat behind _____.
- Ⓐ them
- Ⓑ they
- Ⓒ she
- Ⓓ her

Finding the Answers to Practice 4: Sample

These questions focus mainly on elements of literature, such as character, setting, and plot. Question **A** is a question about a character's feelings. You can find out how Annika feels about Dee and Pam by looking for clues. The story says that Annika liked being around the girls, that they acted cool and said clever things, and that Annika couldn't wait to be like them. These clues show that Annika admires Dee and Pam, so **D** is the correct answer.

Question **B** is a question about setting. The first sentence states that Annika climbed on the school bus, so answer **G** is correct.

Questions about plot ask about what happens in the story. To answer question **C**, you must figure out how Annika felt after listening to Dee and Pam say they had to work all weekend. Annika thought that maybe being older "would not be so terrific after all." **C** is correct.

Question **D** is a question about *figurative language*, which is language that means something different from the literal meaning of the words. To say that Annika "was all ears" means that she listened closely to what they were saying, so answer **G** is correct.

Question **E** is a question about choosing correct pronouns. The pronoun you choose should take the place of *girls*, and it should be an object pronoun. The correct answer is **A**, "them."

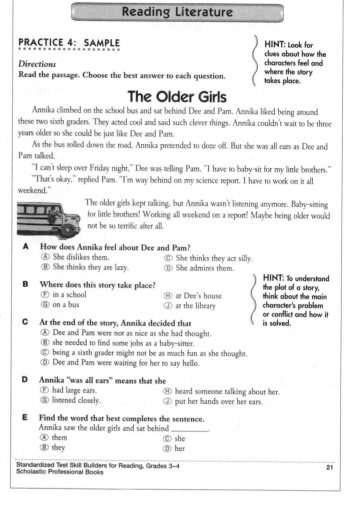

REMINDERS: As you take the Practice Test, remember these hints.

✔ Look for clues in the story to figure out how characters feel and where the story takes place.

✔ To understand the plot, think about the main character's problem or conflict and what he or she does to solve it.

✔ To find the theme of a story, think about what lesson a character learns or what message the author wants to express.

✔ Use clues in the story to determine the meaning of figurative language (such as "all ears").

PRACTICE 4: TEST

Directions
Read the passage. Choose the best answer to each question.

The Brothers and the Cherry Tree

Once upon a time, three brothers lived with their mother in a cottage on the bank of a river. The river was not wide, but it was swift and powerful. Neither the brothers nor the woman had ever attempted to cross it.

Across the river from the cottage stood a magical cherry tree. Every summer, the woman watched the fruit grow and ripen on the tree. When they were deep red and as large as plums, the cherries dropped one by one to the ground. The woman always sighed at this sight, for she longed to eat the magical fruit.

Many summers passed this way, and the brothers became young men. They were tall, strong, and sure of themselves. One day, they noticed their mother staring sadly at the cherry tree. "Mother has given us everything," the brothers said, "so we should give her something in return. Let's find a way to gather cherries from the tree."

The youngest brother, who seldom looked before he leaped, thought that was a great idea. He threw off his shoes, jumped into the water, and started swimming. But the swift, powerful river carried him off.

The middle brother had just a bit more sense than the youngest. With a pocketknife, he cut some branches from a tree. Then he tied them together to make a raft. He put the raft in the river, climbed on, and started paddling with his hands. But the swift, powerful river carried him off, too.

The oldest brother was both clever and careful. He sat down for an hour to think. Then he found an ax and walked along the riverbank, looking at each tree that grew there. He stopped at a tall, strong oak and started chopping it. After a while, he gave the tree a gentle push. It fell across the river to make a sturdy bridge.

Just then the oldest boy saw his two brothers trudging up the riverbank, dripping with water. "You are just in time to gather cherries," he told them. With that, the three brothers walked across the bridge to the other side of the river.

1 **Where does this story take place?**
   (A) in a forest   (C) on a farm
   (B) in a village   (D) near a river

2 **When the woman looked at the cherry tree across the river, she felt**
   (F) peaceful.   (H) sad.
   (G) nervous.   (J) angry.

3 **What did the boys decide to do for their mother?**
   (A) build her a raft
   (B) gather cherries for her
   (C) take her across the river
   (D) build a new cottage for her

4 **The youngest brother "seldom looked before he leaped" means that he**
   (F) closed his eyes and jumped.
   (G) did not think before he acted.
   (H) often swam in the river.
   (J) planned carefully ahead of time.

5 **The events in this story take place during the**
   (A) winter.   (C) summer.
   (B) spring.   (D) fall.

6 **What lesson does this story teach?**
   (F) Careful thinking and planning often lead to success.
   (G) If you have a good idea, keep it to yourself.
   (H) It is selfish to wish for something you cannot have.
   (J) Some people never make mistakes.

7 **What kind of story is this?**
   (A) folktale   (C) biography
   (B) science fiction   (D) historical fiction

Standardized Test Skill Builders for Reading, Grades 3–4
Scholastic Professional Books

8 What problem did the brothers have in this story, and how did they solve it? Write your answer.

_____

_____

Directions
Choose the word that best completes each sentence.

9 The tree is famous for _____ delicious fruit.
Ⓐ it   Ⓒ its
Ⓑ their   Ⓓ they

10 Here is the bridge that _____ crossed.
Ⓕ them   Ⓗ we
Ⓖ him   Ⓙ me

11 Steve picked enough cherries for all of _____.
Ⓐ us   Ⓒ they
Ⓑ we   Ⓓ I

12 Charles fell and hurt _____ leg.
Ⓕ their   Ⓗ him
Ⓖ his   Ⓙ them

SCORE / 12

Making Judgments

PRACTICE 5: SAMPLE

HINT: To make judgments about a passage, think about why the author wrote it.

Directions
Read the passage. Choose the best answer to each question.

A Winning Breakfast

When track star Nora James races, she usually finishes first. What makes Nora a winner? "Every morning I work out at the track for two hours," says Nora. "But first I eat a bowl of Zingers with milk."

Zingers are a delicious blend of oats, rice, corn, and just a touch of honey. These crunchy, golden squares stay crisp to the last spoonful. And just one bowl of Zingers gives you a whole day's supply of ten important vitamins. So if you want to be a winner like Nora James, start your day with Zingers!

A What is the <u>best</u> reason to eat Zingers for breakfast?
  Ⓐ Nora James eats Zingers every morning.
  Ⓑ Zingers supply ten important vitamins.
  Ⓒ You might win something.
  Ⓓ Zingers are square and golden.

HINT: To find an opinion, look for a sentence that states a feeling or belief.

B Which idea from this passage is an opinion?
  Ⓕ Nora usually wins her races.
  Ⓖ Nora works out every morning.
  Ⓗ Zingers taste delicious.
  Ⓙ Zingers are made with honey.

C The author's purpose in this passage is to
  Ⓐ persuade you to buy Zingers.   Ⓒ tell a funny story.
  Ⓑ explain how cereal is made.   Ⓓ give information about Nora James.

D Look at the underlined part of the sentence. Choose the answer that shows the correct capitalization and punctuation.
  Nora <u>says Always</u> start the day with a good breakfast."

  Ⓕ says, Always   Ⓗ says, "always
  Ⓖ says, "Always   Ⓙ Correct as it is

Finding the Answers to Practice 5: Sample

To make judgments, you must ask yourself what the author is trying to say. Think about what kind of information is included, and why.

For question **A**, the passage does not tell you the best reason for eating Zingers, but you can use information from the passage to make your own judgment. You know that the best foods are those that are good for you, so the correct answer is **B**, "Zingers supply ten important vitamins." The other choices do not state good reasons for eating Zingers.

To answer question **B**, you must decide whether each idea from the passage is a fact or an opinion. A fact is an idea that can be proven true, but an opinion is a feeling or belief. Choices F, G, and J are facts that can be proven true. The correct answer, **H**, is the only opinion.

For question **C**, you must think about why the author wrote the passage. This passage is an advertisement written mainly to persuade you to buy Zingers, answer **A**. Passages may also be written mainly to give information, to describe something, or to entertain the reader.

Question **D** is a question about correct capitalization and punctuation of a speaker's words. The correct answer, **G**, uses a comma and quotation marks to set the speaker's words apart from the rest of the sentence, and it begins the quotation with a capital letter.

Making Judgments

PRACTICE 5: SAMPLE

Directions
Read the passage. Choose the best answer to each question.

> HINT: To make judgments about a passage, think about why the author wrote it.

A Winning Breakfast

When track star Nora James races, she usually finishes first. What makes Nora a winner? "Every morning I work out at the track for two hours," says Nora. "But first I eat a bowl of Zingers with milk."

Zingers are a delicious blend of oats, rice, corn, and just a touch of honey. These crunchy, golden squares stay crisp to the last spoonful. And just one bowl of Zingers gives you a whole day's supply of ten important vitamins. So if you want to be a winner like Nora James, start your day with Zingers!

A What is the <u>best</u> reason to eat Zingers for breakfast?
Ⓐ Nora James eats Zingers every morning.
Ⓑ Zingers supply ten important vitamins.
Ⓒ You might win something.
Ⓓ Zingers are square and golden.

> HINT: To find an opinion, look for a sentence that states a feeling or belief.

B Which idea from this passage is an opinion?
Ⓕ Nora usually wins her races.
Ⓖ Nora works out every morning.
Ⓗ Zingers taste delicious.
Ⓙ Zingers are made with honey.

C The author's purpose in this passage is to
Ⓐ persuade you to buy Zingers.   Ⓒ tell a funny story.
Ⓑ explain how cereal is made.   Ⓓ give information about Nora James.

D Look at the underlined part of the sentence. Choose the answer that shows the correct capitalization and punctuation.
Nora <u>says Always</u> start the day with a good breakfast."

Ⓕ says, Always   Ⓗ says, "always
Ⓖ says, "Always   Ⓙ Correct as it is

26   Standardized Test Skill Builders for Reading, Grades 3–4
Scholastic Professional Books

REMINDERS: As you take the Practice Test, remember these hints.

✔ To make a judgment or decision, think about all the details or reasons given. Choose the one that seems most important.

✔ A fact is a statement that can be verified or proven true. To find an opinion, look for a feeling or belief that cannot be proven.

✔ The author's purpose in an advertisement or editorial is to persuade. For most stories, the purpose is to entertain or to teach a lesson. Most other texts are written to inform.

Directions
Read the passage. Choose the best answer to each question.

Computer Games

Are you looking for an exciting computer game that is also educational? Malmo Software has four new games that will knock your socks off!

- **Space Pirate** lets you zoom through the galaxy on your own starship. You will search for treasure, capture aliens, and learn science along the way.

- In **Crazy Cooking,** you make up the recipes, prepare the food, and serve the meals from your own video kitchen. At the same time, you will learn math skills by working with whole numbers, fractions, and measurements.

- **Time Machine** lets you go back to any period in history to see what it was like and find the facts you need to know. You can meet George Washington, sail with Columbus, or even visit cave people!

- **Word Search** takes you on a voyage through the English language—where it began, who invented it, and how it has changed. On your voyage, you will learn new vocabulary and spelling skills.

Each of these new games comes on CD-ROM and costs only $15.95 plus tax. Or, get all four games for only $50! These are the best new games on the planet! They'll provide hours of fun for the whole family. And you'll be amazed at how much you can learn along the way. So don't wait! Order now!

1   **This passage was written mainly to**
   Ⓐ give information about computer games.
   Ⓑ persuade people to buy games.
   Ⓒ explain how CD-ROM games work.
   Ⓓ entertain readers.

2   **Which idea from the passage is an opinion?**
   Ⓕ Malmo Software has four new games.
   Ⓖ Each game comes on CD-ROM.
   Ⓗ Games cost only $15.95 each, plus tax.
   Ⓙ These are the best new games on the planet.

3 If you wanted to know what life was like for the Pilgrims when they landed in America, which game would be the best choice?

Ⓐ "Space Pirate" Ⓒ "Time Machine"
Ⓑ "Crazy Cooking" Ⓓ "Word Search"

4 Which sentence from the passage supports your answer to number 3?

Ⓕ "In Crazy Cooking, you make up the recipes."
Ⓖ "Time Machine lets you go back to any period in history."
Ⓗ "Word Search takes you on a voyage through the English language."
Ⓙ "Space Pirate lets you zoom through the galaxy."

5 You can learn math skills by playing

Ⓐ "Space Pirate." Ⓒ "Time Machine."
Ⓑ "Word Search." Ⓓ "Crazy Cooking."

6 James went to the store and _____ the new games.
Which word suggests that James took a close look at the games?

Ⓕ inspected Ⓗ spotted
Ⓖ noticed Ⓙ saw

Directions
Look at the underlined part of each sentence. Choose the answer that shows the correct capitalization and punctuation for the underlined part. If the underlined part is written correctly, mark "Correct as it is."

7 <u>Yes these</u> new games are great.

Ⓐ Yes! these Ⓒ Yes: these
Ⓑ Yes, these Ⓓ Correct as it is

8 At the store, <u>Mr murdock</u> waited on us.

Ⓕ Mr. Murdock Ⓗ mr. Murdock
Ⓖ Mr Murdock Ⓙ Correct as it is

9 These games help children learn <u>science, math, and history.</u>

Ⓐ science, math and, history Ⓒ science math and history
Ⓑ science math, and history Ⓓ Correct as it is

10 The Malmo Software company is located in <u>ware massachusetts.</u>

Ⓕ Ware Massachusetts Ⓗ Ware, Massachusetts
Ⓖ ware, massachusetts Ⓙ Correct as it is

SCORE / 10

Vocabulary

PRACTICE 6: SAMPLE

HINT: Read the whole paragraph first. Try to think of a word that fits in each blank before you look at the answers.

Directions
Read the passage. For each blank, choose the word that best fits in the sentence.

Many plants can be used as medicine. For example, the juice from an aloe plant will soothe the ___(A)___ of sunburns. If you get poison ivy, the juice from jewelweed will ___(B)___ the itching. Tea made from chamomile helps to settle an upset stomach.

A
- Ⓐ call
- Ⓑ end
- Ⓒ pain
- Ⓓ comfort

B
- Ⓕ stop
- Ⓖ increase
- Ⓗ move
- Ⓙ begin

Choose the word that means the <u>opposite</u> of the underlined word.

C   at the <u>rear</u> of the store
- Ⓐ back
- Ⓑ side
- Ⓒ middle
- Ⓓ front

Choose the word that best completes <u>both</u> sentences.

D   Did you _____ that glass?
Let's take a ten-minute _____.

- Ⓕ fill
- Ⓖ break
- Ⓗ find
- Ⓙ rest

CHAMOMILE

Finding the Answers to Practice 6: Sample

To answer A and B, you must look for clues in the whole paragraph. In question **A**, the only word that fits the meaning of the sentence is "pain" (answer **C**). The answer to question **B** is **F**, "stop."

In question **C**, you must find the *antonym*, or word that means the opposite, of *rear*. The *rear* of the store is the back, so the opposite is "front," answer **D**.

Question **D** is a question about words that have more than one meaning. Each answer choice fits at least one of the sentences. You must find the word that completes *both* sentences correctly. The words *fill* and *find* fit only the first sentence; *rest* fits only the second sentence. The correct answer is **G**, "break"; it fits both sentences.

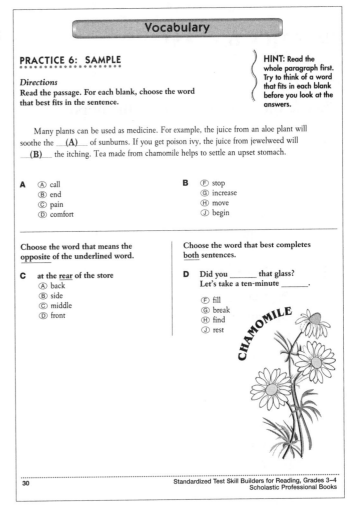

REMINDERS: As you take the Practice Test, remember these hints.

✔ To find a word that fits in a sentence, look for clues in the sentence or sentences before and after the blank.

✔ Try to think of a word that fits in the blank before you look at the answers.

✔ When looking for an antonym, watch out for words that mean the same (such as *rear* and *back* in question C).

✔ For multiple-meaning words, try each answer choice in *both* sentences to see which one fits best.

Vocabulary

PRACTICE 6: TEST

Directions

Choose the word that means the <u>opposite</u> of the underlined word.

1 a <u>huge</u> cloud
- (A) great
- (B) dark
- (C) small
- (D) large

2 staying <u>together</u>
- (F) apart
- (G) between
- (H) around
- (J) close

3 <u>lost</u> a shoe
- (A) tied
- (B) found
- (C) fit
- (D) bought

4 <u>build</u> a bridge
- (F) cross
- (G) construct
- (H) make
- (J) destroy

5 <u>arrive</u> early
- (A) return
- (B) enter
- (C) leave
- (D) come

6 <u>away from</u> the moon
- (F) toward
- (G) after
- (H) separate
- (J) different

Standardized Test Skill Builders for Reading, Grades 3–4
Scholastic Professional Books

Directions
Read the paragraph. For each numbered blank, choose the word that best fits in the sentence.

If you sailed seven miles out from the coast of Florida near Miami, you would see a surprising sight. There are houses standing in the ocean, far from the ___(7)___. They are completely surrounded by ___(8)___. This group of houses is known as "Stiltsville." Each house is ___(9)___ by tall posts called "stilts." At one time there were twenty-five houses in Stiltsville, but now ___(10)___ seven remain. Some environmental groups would like to ___(11)___ the houses because they worry that humans will ___(12)___ the ocean's fragile ecology. But to the people who live there, Stiltsville is home.

7
- Ⓐ fish
- Ⓑ shore
- Ⓒ sea
- Ⓓ waves

8
- Ⓕ crowds
- Ⓖ people
- Ⓗ water
- Ⓙ boats

9
- Ⓐ ruined
- Ⓑ helped
- Ⓒ painted
- Ⓓ supported

10
- Ⓕ always
- Ⓖ only
- Ⓗ although
- Ⓙ even

11
- Ⓐ remove
- Ⓑ enlarge
- Ⓒ remodel
- Ⓓ protect

12
- Ⓕ receive
- Ⓖ accept
- Ⓗ expect
- Ⓙ harm

Read the sentences. Choose the word that best completes <u>both</u> sentences.

13 Mina has a red _____.
The first _____ of paint is dry.

   Ⓐ coat
   Ⓑ hat
   Ⓒ color
   Ⓓ layer

14 Let's _____ our kite.
A _____ landed on my sandwich.

   Ⓕ tie
   Ⓖ bug
   Ⓗ fly
   Ⓙ string

15 I cannot tell a _____.
Dad likes to _____ on the couch.

   Ⓐ sleep
   Ⓑ lie
   Ⓒ story
   Ⓓ tale

16 We will be _____ from the storm.
The bank keeps money in a _____.

   Ⓕ far
   Ⓖ wet
   Ⓗ drawer
   Ⓙ safe

Directions
Choose the word that is spelled correctly to complete the sentence.

17 Mom and Dad really _____ the show.
   Ⓐ enjoyd
   Ⓑ enjoid
   Ⓒ enjoyed
   Ⓓ injoyed

18 Tim helped me _____ the room.
   Ⓕ decarate
   Ⓖ decorate
   Ⓗ decorrate
   Ⓙ deccorate

19 The train pulled into the _____.
   Ⓐ stashun
   Ⓑ stashion
   Ⓒ station
   Ⓓ staton

20 The road crew will _____ with the job.
   Ⓕ proceed
   Ⓖ procede
   Ⓗ proseed
   Ⓙ prosede

SCORE	
	20

Directions

Read each passage. Choose the best answer to each question, or write your answer on the lines.

Just in Case

"Is there going to be a flood?" asked Daniel. He glanced nervously back and forth between his dad and mom. They both looked worried. Dad was soaking wet and dirty. He had just come from the levee down by the river. He and the other men in town had spent the morning piling bags of sand around and on top of the levee. For years this wall of earth had kept the Mississippi from flooding its banks. After three straight days of rain, though, the water was higher than it had ever been. If the levee broke, Daniel's neighborhood would be flooded for sure.

Dad swallowed a bite of his sandwich. "We've done all we can to keep the river out," he said. "The levee seems to be holding up pretty well." He placed a reassuring hand on Daniel's shoulder. "We'll be fine," he said. "You have nothing to worry about."

Daniel felt a little better, but he knew the storm wasn't over yet. Outside, the sky was still very dark. Heavy black clouds hung overhead. Lightning flashed, followed by distant thunder.

Dad frowned. "Just in case," he said, "I think we should start moving some things to Uncle Mike's house." Uncle Mike lived farther away from the river, on higher ground. Dad finished the rest of his sandwich and pushed his chair away from the table. "I'll start loading some things into the pickup truck," he said.

"Daniel and I will start moving some things upstairs," said Mom. She turned to Daniel. "We'll take everything we'll need to cook and eat upstairs—canned goods, pots and pans, a camp stove, a lantern. It'll be fun," she said, "like camping out in our own house."

By nightfall, everything the family needed had been moved upstairs. Dad had taken their new couch, several chairs, and their television set to Uncle Mike's. Before going to bed, Daniel helped his dad move the fishing boat from the backyard and tie it to the front porch. "Just in case," said Dad.

Lying in bed that night, Daniel tossed and turned for quite a while. He could hear the heavy rain beating on the roof. "Everything will be all right," he whispered just before falling asleep.

Several hours later, the sound of sirens woke Daniel from a sound sleep. He sat straight up in bed, his heart pounding. A few minutes later a police car drove slowly through the water in the street. "The levee just broke!" a man shouted through a loudspeaker. "Get out. Get out now!"

Daniel ran to his parents' room. They were already out of bed and getting dressed. "Go get dressed, Daniel," said Mom. "We're leaving. We have no other choice." While Daniel was getting dressed, Mom phoned Uncle Mike to let him know they were coming. Dad went outside to get the boat ready.

A few minutes later they all piled into the fishing boat, leaving behind just about everything they owned. Daniel clutched the family photo album he had thought to grab from the living room on his way out. As they traveled past their neighbors' houses, Daniel shook his head sadly. Already, the water had risen to the first-floor windows. "It's like the whole town is drowning," said Daniel. "We're going to lose everything, aren't we?"

"No, not everything," said Mom, pulling him close. "We'll always have each other," she said.

"That's right," said Dad. "We may lose the house, but we can always rebuild. We can't ever lose our *home*, though, because home is *us*."

Mom smiled and nodded as she gave Daniel another hug.

A few minutes later they spotted Uncle Mike waiting for them on the overpass. They left the fishing boat tied to the bridge, crowded into Uncle Mike's pickup truck, and headed for higher ground.

1 **Where does this story take place?**
Ⓐ in a town near the Mississippi River
Ⓑ on a houseboat
Ⓒ at a police station in Mississippi
Ⓓ at a campground

2 **Daniel's parents were worried that**
Ⓕ the town would run out of sand.
Ⓖ lightning would strike the house.
Ⓗ the river would flood the town.
Ⓙ rain would ruin the crops.

3 **The men piled bags of sand around the levee. What is a levee?**
Ⓐ a place where people go to rent boats
Ⓑ a large body of water where people swim
Ⓒ a box filled with sand for children to play in
Ⓓ a wall of earth built to keep a river from flooding

4 **Daniel had trouble getting to sleep that night because he was**
Ⓕ excited.
Ⓖ sad.
Ⓗ afraid.
Ⓙ sick.

5 **Which sentence best tells what this story is about?**
Ⓐ A man saves a couch and a TV from a flood.
Ⓑ A group of men work together to stop a flood.
Ⓒ A family gets ready in case there's a flood.
Ⓓ A boy and his parents camp out inside their own house.

6 **When Daniel and his parents get to Uncle Mike's house, they most likely will**
  Ⓕ pack all of their things into Uncle Mike's truck.
  Ⓖ help Uncle Mike pile bags of sand around his house.
  Ⓗ wait for news about the flood.
  Ⓙ ask Uncle Mike for some pictures to put in their photo album.

Directions
Choose the word or words that best complete each sentence.

7 **The river is _____ than it has ever been before.**
  Ⓐ high   Ⓒ highest
  Ⓑ higher   Ⓓ most highest

8 **Aunt Bea called and said _____ was leaving.**
  Ⓕ we   Ⓗ us
  Ⓖ she   Ⓙ him

Directions
Daniel wrote a story about the flood. Read the story and then answer questions 9 and 10.

(1) When I woke up in the middle of the night, I knew we were in trouble. (2) Mom, Dad, and I had to wade through the water to get out the front door. (3) The door is blue, and our name is painted on it. (4) We climbed into the boat out front and set off toward Uncle Mike's.

9 **Which sentence best completes Daniel's story?**
  Ⓐ Mom woke up just before I did.
  Ⓑ Our town has not been flooded in the last 35 years.
  Ⓒ We lived near the Mississippi River.
  Ⓓ Water was pouring into the house and rising fast.

10 **Which sentence does <u>not</u> belong in this paragraph?**
  Ⓕ Sentence 1   Ⓗ Sentence 3
  Ⓖ Sentence 2   Ⓙ Sentence 4

Underwater Flyers

Penguins are birds that "fly" underwater. They cannot fly in the air because their bodies are too heavy and their wings too small. The penguin's short, stiff wings are called *flippers*. By flapping these wings the same way birds do in the air, penguins can move through the water just as well as any bird flies through the sky.

Penguins are very different from other birds. Most birds have hollow bones that help make flying easier. The penguins' bones are heavy and solid. This helps them stay underwater. When they aren't flying, most birds can fold their wings close to their bodies, but the penguin's flipper wings hang stiffly from its sides.

All penguins hunt for food underwater. They feed on krill, which live in the ocean and look like shrimp. They also eat squid and many different kinds of fish. No other bird can dive the way a penguin can. Some penguins will dive as deep as 70 feet into the water to get food. Emperor penguins have been known to dive much deeper than that. They can dive deeper than any other bird.

Penguins are very tough birds. Some live in Antarctica, one of the coldest places on Earth. Others live on the Galapagos Islands, a very hot place off the coast of South America. Being too hot or too cold can be a real problem for penguins, but they have learned to adjust. People, though, are the penguin's biggest problem. People and penguins eat some of the same foods. The more fish that people take out of the sea, the fewer there are for the penguins to eat. Also, penguins sometimes get tangled up in fishing nets and die.

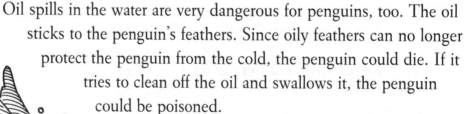

Oil spills in the water are very dangerous for penguins, too. The oil sticks to the penguin's feathers. Since oily feathers can no longer protect the penguin from the cold, the penguin could die. If it tries to clean off the oil and swallows it, the penguin could be poisoned.

Many concerned people are working to help the penguins survive in our modern world. Some help by going to rescue birds in areas where oil spills have occurred. Others have passed laws to protect the penguins and the places where they live.

Standardized Test Skill Builders for Reading, Grades 3–4
Scholastic Professional Books

11 **What is the main idea of this passage?**

Ⓐ Penguins are remarkable birds, but they face many problems caused by people.

Ⓑ Emperor penguins dive deeper than any other bird.

Ⓒ Some people are working hard to save penguins.

Ⓓ Laws have been passed to protect penguins and the places where they live.

12 **How are penguins different from other birds?**

Ⓕ Their bones are hollow.

Ⓖ They cannot flap their wings.

Ⓗ They do not have feathers.

Ⓙ They cannot fly in the air.

13 **Which sentence states an opinion?**

Ⓐ All penguins hunt for food underwater.

Ⓑ Penguins are very tough birds.

Ⓒ People and penguins eat some of the same foods.

Ⓓ The oil sticks to the penguin's feathers.

14 **The passage says that penguins feed on <u>krill</u>. What are <u>krill</u>?**

Ⓕ fishing nets

Ⓖ sea plants

Ⓗ small ocean animals

Ⓙ types of bird seed

15 **Choose the best topic sentence for the paragraph below.**

_____ It is covered by a sheet of ice a mile thick. Very few animals live there because it's too cold.

Ⓐ Spring begins in October in Antarctica.

Ⓑ Richard Byrd made five trips to Antarctica.

Ⓒ Some penguins live in Antarctica, but many live in warmer places.

Ⓓ Antarctica is the coldest place on Earth.

16 **Find the sentence that is complete and is written correctly.**

Ⓕ Fed the penguins.

Ⓖ We saw some penguins at the zoo.

Ⓗ With red eyes and yellow feathers.

Ⓙ Penguins swimming.

The Land of Nod

From breakfast on through all the day
At home among my friends I stay,
But every night I go abroad
Afar into the land of Nod.

All by myself I have to go,
With none to tell me what to do—
All alone beside the streams
And up the mountain-sides of dreams.

The strangest things are there for me,
Both things to eat and things to see,
And many frightening sights abroad
Till morning in the land of Nod.

Try as I like to find the way,
I never can get back by day,
Nor can remember plain and clear
The curious music that I hear.

— Robert Louis Stevenson

Standardized Test Skill Builders for Reading, Grades 3–4
Scholastic Professional Books

17 The speaker of this poem goes to the "Land of Nod" when he is

    (A) dancing.

    (B) sleeping.

    (C) eating.

    (D) reading.

18 This poem was written mainly to

    (F) give information.

    (G) persuade readers to visit Nod.

    (H) teach a lesson.

    (J) entertain readers.

19 From this poem, you can tell that the "Land of Nod" is

    (A) a dreamland.

    (B) very far from Earth.

    (C) a small country.

    (D) near the speaker's home.

Directions

Choose the word that best completes each sentence.

20 Mr. Cortez invited Anna to the museum and gave _____ a tour.

    (F) her

    (G) him

    (H) she

    (J) it

21 Only three children _____ on the school bus.

    (A) is

    (B) was

    (C) are

    (D) am

22 Dad _____ a meat loaf for dinner.

    (F) preppared

    (G) prepaired

    (H) prepareed

    (J) prepared

Living in Space

Shannon Lucid was born on January 14, 1943, in Shanghai, China, to American parents. At the time, China was involved in World War II. When Shannon was just six weeks old, she and her parents were placed in a Japanese prison camp. They were released a year later and returned to the United States, where they settled in Bethany, Oklahoma.

When she was a young girl, Shannon came across a book that helped decide her future. The book was about Robert Goddard, a pioneer in the building of rockets. After reading about Goddard, Lucid knew what she wanted to do.

Shannon Lucid had a real love for space and science. She learned to fly an airplane when she was 20. She also went to the University of Oklahoma to study science. In 1973, when NASA announced that it was looking for women to become astronauts, Lucid signed up right away. She was selected by NASA in January 1978. Lucid was one of the first six American women ever chosen for astronaut training. She became an astronaut in August 1979.

Lucid is a scientist who loves flying. When she was invited to live and work on *Mir*, a Russian space station, it was like a dream come true. Lucid had a lot of work to do to get ready, though. First she had to learn to speak Russian. Then she had to learn all about the space station where she would be living with two Russian cosmonauts. On March 22, 1996, Lucid lifted off from Kennedy Space Center and headed for the *Mir* space station.

Living in a space station 240 miles above the Earth can get pretty boring. How did Lucid pass the time? She spent many hours doing science experiments. She also sent e-mail every day to her husband and grown children, and she read close to fifty books.

Lucid's mission on *Mir* was scheduled to last four and a half months. However, because of bad weather and other problems, she had to stay six weeks longer. She returned to Earth on September 26, 1996. At age 53, Dr. Shannon Lucid had made history. She had spent 188 days in space—an American record.

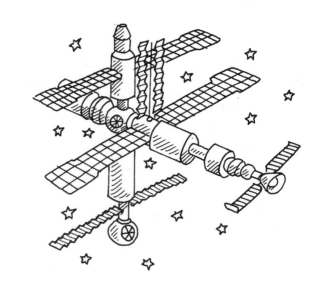

Upon her safe return, Dr. Lucid was honored by President Bill Clinton. The President called her achievement "a monument to the human spirit." She was awarded a Space Medal of Honor in December 1996.

23 **What kind of selection is this?**
- (A) science fiction
- (B) folktale
- (C) historical fiction
- (D) biography

24 **Which word best describes Dr. Lucid?**
- (F) adventurous
- (G) caring
- (H) fearful
- (J) restless

25 **What did Dr. Lucid do first to prepare for her mission on *Mir*?**
- (A) She lifted off from Kennedy Space Center.
- (B) She sent e-mail to her family.
- (C) She learned to speak Russian.
- (D) She learned to fly an airplane.

26 **Dr. Lucid was <u>selected</u> by NASA to become an astronaut. Which word means the same as <u>selected</u>?**
- (F) trained
- (G) encouraged
- (H) discovered
- (J) chosen

Directions

For Questions 27 and 28, choose the answer that uses correct capitalization and punctuation.

> The first space shuttle was launched on ___(27)___. Shuttles are launched from the Kennedy Space Center near ___(28)___.

27
- (A) April 12 1981
- (B) April 12, 1981
- (C) april 12 1981
- (D) april 12, 1981

28
- (F) Orlando Florida
- (G) Orlando, florida
- (H) orlando florida
- (J) Orlando, Florida

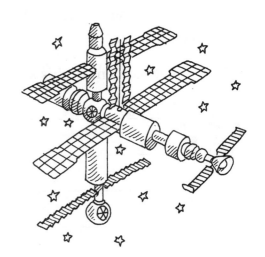

Frog and Locust

A long time ago, the rain did not come for 12 whole months. The grass and the flowers turned brown, and the leaves fell from the trees. In the valley where there was once a river, only a few puddles remained.

Beside one of those puddles lived a small green frog. The frog watched his puddle shrink just a little each day, and he knew the puddle would soon be gone if rain did not come. That would be the end of the frog.

One morning Frog decided to sing a rain song, and that's what he did. For fifteen minutes Frog croaked and croaked, but no rain came. The rain god lived atop a high mountain and could not hear the song.

In a bush nearby lived a small brown locust. The locust knew that if rain did not come soon, he would die. So the locust sang a rain song, too. For 15 minutes he buzzed and buzzed, but the rain god could not hear him, either. When Locust realized that no rain was going to fall, he became so sad that he started to cry.

Frog heard the locust crying and hopped over to the bush. "What's wrong?" asked Frog. When Locust explained what he was crying about, Frog began to cry, too. Together they made quite a racket, and the noise gave Locust an idea.

"Maybe we should sing our songs together," said Locust. Frog immediately agreed, and they began to sing.

With two voices, the rain song was louder than before. But still the sound did not reach the ears of the rain god.

All over the valley, however, other frogs and locusts heard the song. Every frog began to croak, and every locust began to buzz. The creatures sang so loud that, at last, the rain god heard the song. He gathered up as many dark clouds as he could find, and the rain began to fall.

Soon the river was all filled up again, the trees got their leaves back, and the grass turned green. The world came back to life once more—thanks to Frog and Locust, who decided to join their voices in song.

29 What happens in this story? Write a short summary of what happens.

Standardized Test Skill Builders for Reading, Grades 3–4
Scholastic Professional Books

30 You would be most likely to find this story in a

Ⓕ newspaper.

Ⓖ collection of folktales.

Ⓗ science textbook.

Ⓙ encyclopedia.

31 The story says that frog watched his puddle <u>shrink</u> a little each day. Which word means the *opposite* of <u>shrink</u>?

Ⓐ dry

Ⓑ wilt

Ⓒ move

Ⓓ grow

32 What lesson can be learned from this story?

Ⓕ Working together is better than working alone.

Ⓖ People who try too hard usually fail.

Ⓗ Good things come to those who wait.

Ⓙ Animals and people do not get along.

33 Which of these is a complete sentence?

Ⓐ Many frogs living in the pond.

Ⓑ A colorful fish in the water.

Ⓒ Two large frogs rested on a log.

Ⓓ Peeping and croaking all night long.

Directions

For questions 34 and 35, choose the sentence that is written correctly.

34 Ⓕ Raquel and I met last year at a summer camp.

Ⓖ Raquel is from brazil, and I'm from new york.

Ⓗ We shared a cabin and get to know each other really well.

Ⓙ This year we won't be sharing a cabin, but we'll still be friends.

35 Ⓐ Claire wants to be a scientist someday.

Ⓑ Her and Mary went to the science museum.

Ⓒ Claire and her friend both likes to study plants.

Ⓓ Everybody are going on a field trip next week.

36 Find the sentence that best combines these two sentences into one.

Derek loves camping.

Derek doesn't enjoy hiking.

Ⓕ Derek loves camping, and he doesn't enjoy hiking.

Ⓖ Derek loves camping, he doesn't enjoy hiking.

Ⓗ Derek loves camping, but he doesn't enjoy hiking.

Ⓙ Derek loves camping or doesn't enjoy hiking.

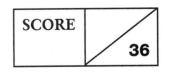

SCORE / 36

Answer Key

Getting the Main Idea
PRACTICE 1: TEST

1. B
2. F
3. D
4. G
5. A
6. H
7. C
8. G
9. B
10. G
11. C
12. F

Understanding Texts
PRACTICE 2: TEST

1. B
2. J
3. C
4. F
5. C
6. J
7. B
8. **Examples:** His mother taught him at home; she made learning fun; he could ask questions; she let him do experiments.
9. B
10. F
11. D
12. H

Making Inferences
PRACTICE 3: TEST

1. D
2. G
3. B
4. H
5. D
6. G
7. **Example:** At the beginning, Danny thought he would hate staying at Aunt Grace's and did not like the idea of going out on a rainy night. By the end, he thought the night of the salamander crossing was great fun and hoped he could count salamanders again the next year.
8. G
9. D
10. H

Reading Literature
PRACTICE 4: TEST

1. D
2. H
3. B
4. G
5. C
6. F
7. A
8. **Example:** They wanted to get some cherries for their mother, but they could not swim or raft across the river. The oldest brother cut a tree that fell across the river, and they used it as a bridge.
9. C
10. H
11. A
12. G

Standardized Test Skill Builders for Reading, Grades 3–4
Scholastic Professional Books

Answer Key, continued

Making Judgments
PRACTICE 5: TEST

1. B
2. J
3. C
4. G
5. D
6. F
7. B
8. F
9. D
10. H

Vocabulary
PRACTICE 6: TEST

1. C
2. F
3. B
4. J
5. C
6. F
7. B
8. H
9. D
10. G
11. A
12. J
13. A
14. H
15. B
16. J
17. C
18. G
19. C
20. F

READING TEST

1. A
2. H
3. D
4. H
5. C
6. H
7. B
8. G
9. D
10. H
11. A
12. J
13. B
14. H
15. D
16. G
17. B
18. J
19. A
20. F
21. C
22. J
23. D
24. F
25. C
26. J
27. B
28. J
29. **Example:** It had not rained for a year, so Frog and Locust sang a rain song. Nothing happened, but when all the frogs and locusts sang together, the rain came.
30. G
31. D
32. F
33. C
34. J
35. A
36. H